Jarrold Nature Series
Photographs and text by
Heather Angel, MSc, FIIP, FRPS

Life in our
Rivers

D1610895

Jarrold Colour Publications, Norwich

1. RIVER ETIVE, SCOTLAND. Here is a typical trout reach of a river flowing down a glaciated U-shaped valley. The deep pools offer sheltered hide-outs to the fish.

Since there are over 200 main river systems in mainland Britain, everyone lives within a few miles of a river or one of its tributaries. It is not always easy to make a clear-cut distinction between a river and a stream. Near their mouths, rivers are clearly much wider and deeper than streams; but rivers often originate as small streams. As streams merge one with another, their combined waters contribute towards the formation of a distinct river. The place where a river originates is known as its source. This may be from a mountain tarn, an underground spring, a limestone rock fissure or from water seeping through boggy ground. Whatever their source, rivers start life on higher ground than where their mouth leads into the sea. Little streams tumble down steep mountain-sides carrying cold, pure, well-oxygenated water, collecting more water from mossy flushes and other secondary rivulets. The mosses and algae which cover the stones are fed on by the larvae of midges, stoneflies and caddis-flies. Some of the caddis-fly larvae weave webs to strain their food from the current. All the animals are adapted to clinging on to stones and vegetation to stop themselves being swept away by the rapid flow.

As the river grows, so pools become deep enough for them not to dry up in a normal summer and trout begin to occur. Gravel reaches offer spawning beds for salmon, trout and brook lampreys. Male bullheads, on the other hand, stand guard over the eggs laid by the female on the underside of stones and boulders. Initially the newly hatched larval fish are sustained by their yolk sac, but when that is exhausted they start to feed on the insect larvae, small snails and freshwater shrimps in the river, and other insects that fall into the river from the air above.

The type of terrain the river flows through will determine the variety of its animal and plant inhabitants. A river rising and flowing through sandstone or granite will have soft, slightly acidic water and contain few, if any, snails, whereas a river flowing through limestone will have hard, slightly akaline water and will contain a rich snail fauna. The types of insect larvae, worms and leeches will also vary according to the water quality. Similarly, water draining from old mine workings and tips may contain high levels of metals in solution which are too toxic for many of the river inhabitants.

The geological history of an area also affects the character of its rivers. Normally a river cuts a steep-sided V-shaped valley into a hillside. But in Europe during the last Ice Age, which ended 12,000 years ago, the glaciers gouged deep U-shaped valleys, and truncated the feeder valleys. So that in the mountains, the waterfalls now tumble down the sheer sides of the glaciated valleys, to feed a rather small stream meandering along the flat floor of an imposing valley. In the lowlands, series of gravel beds perched several metres above the present river level, mark ancient river courses and emphasise how transient our landscape is in terms of geological time.

As the river flows on, the gradient of the bed becomes gentler, the current flow slackens sufficiently to allow submerged plants to grow and the stream-side plants become more lush. This is called the grayling zone. Other fish that abound are trout, minnow, chub, barbel and gudgeon. The water tends to be warmer, and this, together with the slowing of the swirling currents, means that the amount of oxygen in the water is not quite so high. The slowing current also results in the river bed becoming sandy or even muddy in quiet backwaters. Run off from surrounding agricultural land enriched with fertilisers may tend to change the river's character, encouraging the growth of the plants and the increase in numbers of coarse fish, like roach, dace and rudd. Several of Britain's trout streams are maintained only by a constant management programme of electro-fishing out the coarse fish and re-stocking with trout. However, the richer vegetation encourages an abundance of insect life to inhabit the river. Mayfly larvae, with their delicate three-pronged tails, sometimes hatch in such profusion that motorists on nearby roads are brought to a halt unable to see through their windscreens. At the time of a big hatch, the trout feed in a frenzy as they attempt to gobble down the sudden superabundance of food. Not so pleasant are the small blackflies, the females of which suck blood. These biting flies, known in Speyside as birch flies, are a pest not only to man, but also to cattle.

As the river broadens and slows still further, it becomes a typical lowland river meandering sluggishly through a flat countryside. The water is much more turbid because it now contains thousands of microscopic plant cells in every litre. There is an abundance of animal plankton consisting of ciliate protozoans, rotifers with their wheels of fine beating hairs or cilia, and little crustaceans such as water fleas and *Cyclops*. Oxygen levels are lower and the bottom becomes muddy. The common fish are carp, roach, tench, bream, sticklebacks and loach. In the weed beds live river snails, freshwater shrimps, water lice, a variety of leeches that feed on the snails and the insect larvae, water beetles and saucer bugs. The muds are inhabited by tiny relatives of the earthworm called tubifex worms, midge or chironomid larvae, and bivalve molluscs like the pea-mussels and swan mussels. Well-known birds associated with rivers are duck, moorhens and kingfishers; while fringing reed-beds are frequented by an assortment of insect-eating birds such as warblers and buntings. Water voles live in holes in the banks, holes which in turn may be occupied underwater by freshwater crayfish. Otters which used to abound in our lowland rivers, are too shy to thrive in our heavily managed rivers. Now, an introduced carnivore – the mink – is spreading along our river systems.

These sluggish, lowland rivers are under the heaviest pressure from man's activities. Water is drawn off to fill reservoirs; and, in estuarine stretches in particular, to condense the steam used to drive power-station turbines. This so-called cooling water, which becomes warmed by as much as 10 °C, affects the flora and fauna in the immediate discharge area. Warm water carries less oxygen than cold water. The oxygen level is also reduced if too much raw or semi-treated sewage is pumped into the river, since bacterial activity utilises the oxygen in the water. The bottom mud then becomes black owing to the production of hydrogen sulphide, a highly toxic gas smelling of bad eggs. Rivers are also used for transport and leisure activities. They may be dammed to make reservoirs or to generate hydro-electric power. Flood-control measures involve the removal of bankside vegetation, the reinforcement of banks and straightening of channels.

The authorities responsible for the water quality of our rivers now recognise these threats to our riverine life. In England the River Thames was once so polluted with domestic sewage, that during hot summers paint was blackened by the hydrogen sulphide several miles away from the river. A major campaign was launched to clean up the Thames. Sewage plants were enlarged and improved, and certain types of industrial effluent were banned. Now, many dozens of different kinds of fish have been reported from the river as it flows through London. The Thames at one time had been a salmon river, the mature fish migrating up the river from their feeding grounds in the deep ocean, to spawn in the head waters of the river. Salmon runs are restricted to the cleanest rivers, so the re-establishment of a run in the Thames is the eventual goal of the cleaning-up programme. Salmon are not the only fish that move between rivers and the sea. Sea trout and sea lampreys also feed at sea, returning to the river to spawn. Eels, in contrast, spawn in the deeps of the Sargasso Sea and it takes three years for the larvae to drift across the Atlantic to European shores. They are then known as elvers and large numbers move up our rivers in the spring. There they feed and mature before moving downstream on moonlit nights back again to the sea. Fishes which make such migrations have to undergo considerable physiological changes to withstand the change from salt to fresh water.

Figures in red beside each illustration indicate the scale of magnification.

2

2. AFON ELAN. Sunlight glinting on the surface of this river in the mid-Wales mountains, emphasises the pattern of the river meanders. Even in flood, the river is far too small to have eroded such a big valley. The U-shaped valley indicates its glacial origin and the ridges of gravel and boulders are old moraines. Here, the waters offer the trout fishermen ideal conditions for fly-fishing. Lower down, the pure mountain water is stored in the huge Elan Valley reservoirs.

3. RIVER WYE NEAR BUILTH WELLS. During a dry summer, this famous salmon river was photographed when its water level was unusually low. The scattered boulders and gravel stretches are typical of the trout reaches of many large rivers. The main salmon run is in the autumn, but the larger fish move up the river in the very early spring months to spawn in the head waters high up in the Welsh mountains. The river also offers excellent fishing for brown trout which are resident all the year round. The current is normally far too fierce for flowering plants to grow in the water; even the banks are too well scoured by the winter floods for emergent vegetation to flourish. As a result, there is no protection from the current for invertebrate animals, such as insect larvae and snails which live under or between the boulders. They tend to have flattened bodies and cling very tightly to the surface of the rocks. Even there, they are not safe from attack by fish and also dippers – lively little brown birds which can run straight down into the water.

4

4. RIVER ITCHEN, HAMPSHIRE. This exceptionally beautiful lowland river rises on chalk near Alresford. Its cool, spring-fed water contains dissolved calcium carbonate, so that it supports a particularly rich fauna of snails and insect larvae, which in turn find ample food and shelter in among the beds of water crowfoot, shown here flowering in May. Such unpolluted chalk streams are famed for their trout and also have good salmon runs. Salmon can be seen leaping on the Itchen Navigation at Bishopstoke. Watercress is cultivated in many of the feeder streams in special beds where the water levels are carefully regulated. The freshwater shrimp (19) is one of the pests of these beds, since it damages the cress and makes it less attractive for market. The Itchen flows out into Southampton Water making the transition from an idyllic trout stream into a very busy industrialised waterway.

5. THE HAMPSHIRE AVON, NEAR FORDINGBRIDGE. This is a chalk river that winds its way through old water meadows. These meadows used to be purposely flooded to provide fresh green grass for cattle throughout the summer. The Avon supports coarse fish typical of faster reaches, like minnows, chub and dace, as well as others usually occurring in sluggish water such as roach and pike. A 47 ℔ (21 kg) pike was caught nearby in 1944. Bottom-feeding fish such as the brook lamprey, stone loach, bullhead, gudgeon and barbel are common. The banks of the Avon are riddled with the burrows of water voles, which feed on the riverside vegetation. The water shrew is particularly common in and around the ditches that feed the Avon.

6. FLOWERING RUSH (*Butomus umbellatus*). One of the more attractive riverside plants is the flowering rush, which is locally known as Pride of the Thames and Raxen in different

5

6 ×0·3

parts of Britain. It is locally common in southern and central Britain, but is rare in Wales and absent from highland Scotland. It is widespread in Europe and was introduced into North America, where it has established itself along the St Lawrence and round the Great Lakes. It is a perennial plant with edible underwater rhizomes. The leaves, which are sharp and will cut the mouths of grazing cattle, and flowering heads grow upwards out of the water. In July to September, the flowers open to reveal the bright red stamens against the attractive pink petals. It is a plant that is particularly resistant to flooding and often survives better than other aquatic plants. The seeds are intermittent in their germination, and are slightly fragrant. They were once used to help people relax before sleeping.

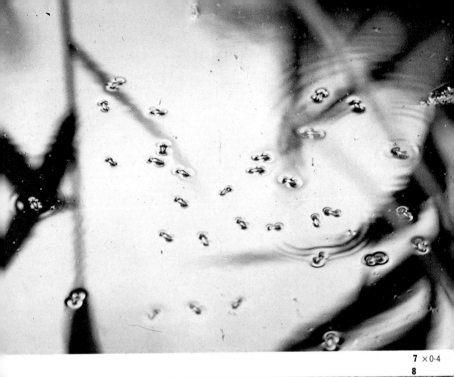

7 ×0.4
8

7. WHIRLIGIG BEETLES (*Gyrinus marinus*). In quiet backwaters, where there is little current, groups of whirligigs gyrate on the surface. When they sense vibrations on the water surface caused by a drowning insect, they dash towards this potential food source. These beetles are efficient swimmers which dive to avoid danger, using their hair-fringed second and third pairs of legs. Their eyes are divided into two parts, so that one part looks above the water surface, while the other watches below. The eggs are laid on submerged plants and the carnivorous larvae crawl over the bottom. They pupate in cocoons of mud attached to the plants. The adults hatch in late summer and on warm summer evenings they readily fly, and are frequently attracted in large numbers to lights near rivers.

8. MALLARDS (*Anas platyrhynchos*). Mallards are the most widespread of our ducks. During the winter, groups of drakes assemble and undergo elaborate courtship rituals to attract the ducks. Once a duck and a drake have paired, they remain together for the rest of the year. Nesting starts in February, either on the ground or low down in a riverside tree. Only the duck incubates the 7–16 eggs, which hatch after twenty-eight days. The ducklings are immediately led to the water by the mother. Many are taken by a variety of predators, including pike. Few of this flotilla of ducklings will survive the six weeks before they are fledged.

9. MUTE SWANS (*Cygnus olor*). Swans are perhaps the most familiar of all our aquatic birds. Here, the male (cob) stands guard over the cygnets while they feed below the surface on aquatic plants. Both parents look after the cygnets until they are fledged, four months after they hatch. Swans became semi-domesticated because of their decorative value and use as a luxury food. Over 900 swan marks were recognised during the reign of Elizabeth I. Any unmarked swan automatically belonged to the crown.

9

10 ×2·5
11 ×2

10. MAYFLY LARVA (*Ephemera vulgata*). Mayfly larvae, or nymphs, can be recognised by their three tail processes. This nymph lives burrowed in the sand and mud of stream beds, feeding on detritus and microscopic algae. The pair of long tusklike mandibles and the short powerful forelegs are modified for digging. The gills are the plumes arching over the back of the abdomen. As they beat they create a constant current of water through the burrow and over the gills. Other stream-dwelling mayfly nymphs are either flattened, and crawl about among the gravel and mosses on the stream bed; or are torpedo-shaped active swimmers. The nymphs are important items in the diets of many fish and carnivorous invertebrates. These burrowing species of mayfly usually spend two years as larvae before emerging.

11. MAYFLY DUN (*Ephemera danica*). When the nymphs are ready to hatch, they leave their burrows and swim to the surface of the stream. The back of the thorax swells and suddenly splits, so the sub-imago, or dun, emerges. All the duns of each kind of mayfly tend to emerge during a short period, known as a hatch. During a hatch the surface of the stream becomes littered with the newly emerged duns and their shucks – the cast nymphal skins. Trout, oblivious to all danger, gorge themselves, and anglers mimic the duns with their wet flies. The duns take to the air, flying tail-heavy downwind. They settle on nearby vegetation and hide away. Mayfly duns are the only winged non-adult insects and they soon moult again to become adults. A moulting dun spreads its wings out sideways, the thorax splits and the adult, or spinner, emerges.

12. MAYFLY SPINNER (*Ephemera danica*). Compared with the dun, this stage has darker markings and much longer tail processes. On warm summer evenings, mating swarms of spinners are common near unpolluted rivers. Large numbers of males congregate, performing dancing flights, flying up a metre or two, then parachuting down with their wings outspread. A female entering the swarm is mated in the air and almost immediately flies to the water to lay her eggs. In this species, the eggs are laid in batches while the female rests momentarily on the water surface. She then dies. Spent spinners are also eaten by trout. So fly-fishermen mimic them with their dry flies. A dry fly is cast so that it sits on the water surface and the trout is lured to rise and take it; whereas a wet fly sinks. Fly-fishermen call the dun of *Ephemera danica* the Green Drake and the spinner the Grey Drake.

12 ×2·5

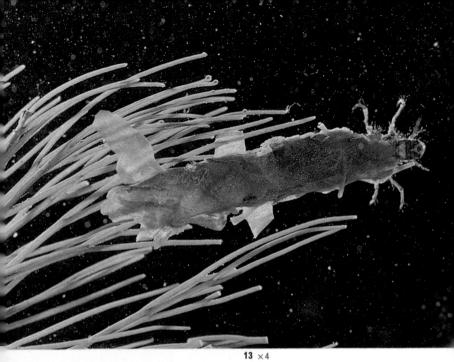

13 ×4
14 ×2·5

13. CADDIS-FLY LARVA. The larvae of all but one of the 200 species of British caddis-flies are aquatic. The eggs are laid by the moth-like adults in or near water. The female may crawl beneath the water to lay flat sheets of eggs under stones or on water weeds. Many of the larvae construct a protective case round themselves made from sand, or leaves as shown in this picture. Other types of caddis larvae spin nets under stones or on plant stems to trap tiny animals. Prior to pupating, the larva plugs the opening of its case or weaves a tough silken cocoon. Eventually the pupa breaks itself free and swims to the surface to hatch into the adult. Despite their protective cases, some caddis larvae are parasitised before they pupate by a tiny ichneumon fly which crawls underwater to lay its eggs.

14. ALDER-FLY LARVA (*Sialis lutaria*). One of the more attractive insect larvae that occurs among the weeds of slowly flowing streams, is the alder-fly. The larvae take nearly two years to grow to their full size of about 2·5 cm (1 in.). The powerful jaws show these active burrowers to be carnivorous, and they attack many kinds of other insect larvae. Along the back of the abdomen are the long paired gills which constantly beat to maintain a flow of water. When they are mature the larvae crawl out of the water, sometimes as far as 200 metres away to burrow into damp soil where they pupate. After three weeks' pupation the adult hatches, usually in May or early June.

15. ADULT ALDER-FLY (*Sialis lutaria*) **RESTING ON SEDGE.** The dark brown adults with their long antennae and heavily veined wings spend much of their time resting on streamside plants, and it is their association with alders which gave rise to their colloquial name. They are clumsy fliers and many drown by falling into the water. The jaws are weak and so they are able only to take fluids. The females lay blocks of 500–600 brown eggs on the stems of emergent plants. Ten to fourteen days later the newly hatched larvae drop off the plants into the water below to start the life cycle anew. If the egg cases are examined with a hand-lens after the larvae have hatched, most of them will have a longitudinal slit. However, a few have small round holes. These have been parasitised by a tiny hymenopteran wasp. Alder-flies are particularly abundant along the minnow reaches of our rivers where submerged plants like starwort and water crowfoot grow well and there is an abundance of insect life in the water for the larvae to feed on.

15 ×3

16. DEMOISELLE AGRION (*Agrion virgo*). This beautiful damselfly prefers fast-flowing streams with sand or gravel bottoms, especially if they are tree-lined and have slightly acidic water. *A. splendens* is a related species which has bi-coloured wings. These damselflies catch insects in flight by using their hairy forelegs rather like a net. Egg-laying occurs when the male and female are in tandem, the female dipping her abdomen well below the water surface, attaching the eggs to the weeds. The iridescent colours are formed by the structure of the wing.

17. BANDED AGRION NYMPH (*Agrion splendens*). The nymphs of the two species are very similar. They are stiff-legged and rather spider-like in appearance. The jaw is mounted on a folding mask which can be shot forward to grab its prey of insect larvae and other small animals. These damselflies take two years to mature.

18. GOLDEN-RINGED DRAGON-FLY (*Cordulegaster boltoni*). This female darter dragonfly is laying her eggs in a New Forest river, dipping her abdomen into the water while hovering. Darter dragonflies are powerful piratical fliers, catching their insect prey on the wing. The males are territorial, and during the summer months they ceaselessly patrol their patch, fighting any intruders. Constant battles leave them very battered towards the end of summer. The larvae of these dragonflies are clumsy but effective predators which are able to kill and eat fish as long as themselves. They are grotesque mud-dwellers, covered with dense hairs to which mud and debris adhere. They lie in the mud with the head showing and also the tip of the abdomen arched above the mud surface.

17 × 3
18 × 0·8

19. **FRESHWATER SHRIMP** (*Gammarus pulex*). These amphipods, which grow to about a centimetre in length, are relatives of the seaside sandhoppers. They occur abundantly in well-oxygenated water which is not too acidic. By day they mostly hide away beneath stones, emerging at night to scavenge for food. In spring, the females carry their eggs in a brood pouch under the thorax. The larvae, which are miniature replicas of the adults, stay in the brood pouch for a further week.

20. **PURPLE LOOSESTRIFE** (*Lythrum salicaria*). From June until September the handsome spikes of purple loosestrife decorate our river banks. One of the most unusual features of this plant is that there are three types of flower, each with styles and stamens of different lengths. The pollen grains also differ in size, the largest grains being produced by the longest stamens. This mechanism ensures cross-pollination must take place.

21. STONEFLY LARVA (*Perlodes microcephala*). This stonefly nymph is typical of stony lowland rivers. Stonefly larvae are mostly bottom dwellers, feeding chiefly on vegetable detritus. They occur only in well-oxygenated water and are easily distinguished from other aquatic insect larvae by their two tail processes.

22. YELLOW SALLY (*Isoperla grammatica*). This adult stonefly is one of the most widespread and abundant British species. It emerges in late spring and summer. The females crawl underwater to lay their gelatinous egg masses. Hatching from a single egg mass is staggered, and initially the larvae grow very little; rapid growth to maturity occurs only after several months.

19 ×4
20 ×0·4

21 ×2·5
22 ×3

23. FRESHWATER CRAYFISH (*Astacus pallipes*). These nocturnal animals occur only in chalk or limestone rivers. They are general carnivores which spend the day hidden away in weed beds, under stones or in holes in the river bank. The female lays her eggs in autumn and carries them attached beneath her abdomen. Behind the crayfish can be seen some willow moss which grows in rivers attached to stones.

24. WANDERING SNAIL (*Limnaea pereger*). This snail grazes both on waterweeds and on the microscopic algae that grow over stream-bed stones. Each snail is hermaphrodite and lays gelatinous egg masses. The snails have been known to move upstream at 2-4 km per year to re-colonise stretches in which flash pollution had killed the previous inhabitants.

25. BULLHEAD OR MILLER'S THUMB (*Cottus gobio*). Adult bullheads are solitary except in the breeding season. They are important predators of trout eggs. Notice how well this one blends in with the bottom gravel.

23 ×0·8

24 ×1·5
25 ×1

26. TROUT ALEVINS (*Salmo trutta*). The brown trout is one of the most highly prized sporting fishes in British rivers, second only to the salmon. Trout live mainly in the cool, well-oxygenated waters of our more mountainous regions, and the spring-fed chalk streams. In winter, the adults move upstream, seeking gravel reaches. There the female or hen fish excavates, by frantically beating her tail, a shallow depression in the gravel which is called a redd. When complete, the male or cock moves in alongside the hen fish to fertilise her eggs with his milt. The eggs, which are then buried in a layer of gravel, take forty days to hatch at 10 °C and longer if the water temperature is cooler. The newly hatched larvae are called alevins. For the first few weeks of life they feed on the yolk in the yellow yolk sac. When the yolk is exhausted, they begin to feed on live food. After three months they become fry.

27. TROUT FRY (*Salmo trutta*). At this stage, the fish are beginning to develop the dark marks on each side of the body. When these marks are fully developed, the fish is known as a parr. As the fish matures, red and blackish spots appear on the back and flanks. The adults mature in three to four years when they have reached a length of about 25 cm (10 in.). However, the rate of growth depends very much on the temperature of the water and the richness of the food. Fish from the River Kennet were over 27 cm (10·5 in.) after three years, but those from the River Dart only 17 cm (7 in.). Their food consists mainly of insects, crustaceans and snails, while a few fish may become cannibalistic. The brown trout is a highly variable species. One particularly interesting variant is the sea trout, which moves downstream and out to sea to feed. Commercial hatcheries now breed thousands of trout fingerlings for re-stocking rivers, as well as lakes. Eggs which are stripped from the ripe hen fish are fertilised by stripping milt from the cock fish into the same container. After thorough mixing, the eggs are washed in water and placed in trays in a running water system. Trout and salmon are aged by counting the number of 'rings' on their scales, formed by narrow ridges laid down during winter, alternating with widely spaced summer ridges.

26 ×2

28. PERCH (*Perca fluviatilis*). Perch are coarse fish that occur in ponds, lakes and rivers. They are rather sedentary fish that usually aggregate in mixed-sized shoals close to the piles of jetties, bridges and tree roots. The barred colour of the flanks helps to break up the body outline and camouflage it underwater. They are active carnivores, feeding on small planktonic crustaceans and insect larvae when young, but eating progressively larger and larger prey as they grow. The largest individuals tend to be solitary and feed extensively on other fish like bleak and young roach. In April and May individual females, accompanied by several males, move into the shallows to spawn. The eggs are entwined around underwater plants as a delicate lacework.

29. DETAIL OF PERCH SPAWN (*Perca fluviatilis*). Each female may lay up to 300,000 eggs which hatch after about a fortnight. Initially the young fish are very dependent on a regular supply of plankton and they gradually scatter. Once they reach a length of 2 cm, they begin to form large shoals. They reach maturity in 2–3 years. Perch are good fighting fish for the angler. They can be caught by spinning, ledgering with lobworms or by live-baiting with minnow or small roach. Perch is a highly favoured fish in continental Europe, where it is sold fresh, dried or salted. Probably over 20,000 tons are caught each year commercially in Europe, using a variety of techniques ranging from traps and stake nets to purse seines. An experimental fishery was started in Lake Windermere during the 1939–45 war, the catch being sold for canning. In the River Thames near Reading, measurements have shown that there are about 66 g of perch, roach, dace and bleak per square metre of river bed, the annual production of fish being about 42 g per square metre.

28 ×0·5

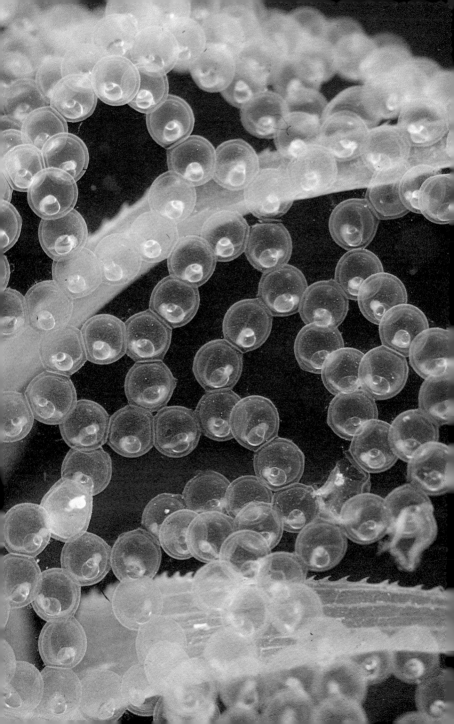

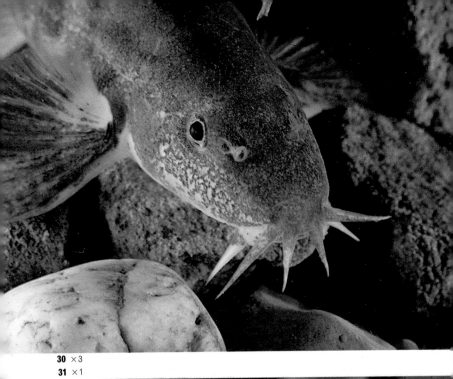

30 ×3
31 ×1

30. STONE LOACH (*Noemacheilus barbatulus*). The fringe of barbels round the mouth of the stone loach indicates that it is a bottom-living fish. The barbels are used to grub out shrimps, insect larvae and worms from the stream bed. Stone loaches are mostly nocturnal and spend the day hidden away in among thick weed beds or under stones. They are solitary, only coming together to spawn in April and May. Males and females both develop spawning tubercles on the inner sides of their pectoral fins. The sticky eggs are shed either among gravel or weed. One female may lay more than half a million eggs, which take about a fortnight to hatch into 3 mm long larvae. Most are sexually mature at the end of their first year of life when they are about 8 cm (3·5 in.) long. However, they may take five years to reach their maximum length of 11·5 cm (4·5 in.). The stone loach is preyed on by a variety of other fish, including trout, pike and eels. They are also taken by otters and when young by water shrews. Since they are sensitive to pollution, they can be used as indicators of pure water. They have no economic value as they are too small.

31 and 32. RIVER LAMPREY (*Lampetra fluviatilis*). Lampreys are very primitive jawless fish which feed as external parasites on other fish. The sucker-like mouth is able to clamp on to other fish and rasp away at their flesh. The lamprey can continue to pump water over its gills while it is feeding, because the seven pairs of open gill slits lie well behind the head. These eel-like fish start life as ammocoete larvae buried in rich organic mud and feed on fine particles which they sieve from the water. After five years they metamorphose into the adult form and migrate down to the sea.

32 × 4

They spend a year feeding at sea and increasing their length four times to approximately 50 cm (20 in.). They migrate back up the rivers when the gut atrophies and they become sexually mature. They spawn in early spring when the water temperature is 12 °C. The male excavates a nest in sandy gravel into which the female lays about 20,000 eggs. Two other types of lamprey occur in British rivers, the brook lamprey and the sea lamprey. The brook lamprey grows to a maximum length of 15 cm (6 in.). It spends its whole life in fresh water. The larvae mature into adults which do not feed at all. In contrast, the sea lamprey spends one to two years as an adult at sea, feeding parasitically on a variety of fishes and reaches a maximum length of 80 cm (32 in.). Such large predators can cause extensive injury to their prey. In the United States the building of a canal by-passing the St Lawrence to the Great Lakes, introduced the sea lamprey into the Lakes. This resulted in the lampreys destroying a profitable fishery.

33. GRAYLING (*Thymallus thymallus*). This is a sporting fish of cool well-oxygenated rivers with strong currents. It often occurs in small shoals feeding on insect larvae, freshwater shrimps and fry of other fish. Grayling spawn in March to May in shallow gravel on sandy reaches, the eggs taking about three weeks to hatch. They are excellent to eat when fresh but they rapidly spoil. They are also extremely sensitive to pollution and an increase in water temperature. The best sites for hydro-electric schemes are usually in the grayling reaches of rivers, so that many European rivers have lost their grayling.

34. THREE-SPINED STICKLEBACKS (*Gasterosteus aculeatus*). The study of nesting and courtship display by these aggressive little fish was one of the classic pieces of behavioural science. Here, the male is shown below the female, in his colourful breeding dress. Sticklebacks play an important part in the economy of rivers, in that they compete for the food of the young, more valued fish, but in turn are fed on by herons and kingfishers. They are one of the most widely distributed of all British freshwater fishes, being absent only from fast-flowing hill streams. They can tolerate quite salty water and so are common in many estuaries, as well as in the sea off Scotland and Northern Ireland.

35. TENCH (*Tinca tinca*). This is a shy bottom-living fish of slow-moving muddy rivers. It feeds on insect larvae and snails, sensing them in the murky water with the mouth barbels. Tench are very resistant to poorly oxygenated water, and overwinter by lying dormant in the bottom mud. They spawn in summer, usually in shallow water where the vegetation is thick. Tench are also noted for their very slimy covering of mucus.

33 ×0·3

34 ×1·5

35 ×0·3

36. LITTLE GREBE (*Tachybaptes ruficollis*). In early summer the trilling courtship songs of the little grebes or dabchicks echo along the quieter waterways. These attractive birds, which are shy and retiring, are much more abundant than most people realise. They are great divers, catching their food of sticklebacks, shrimps and aquatic insects while swimming underwater. At the approach of danger they can squeeze air out of the feathers so that only the beak and nostrils project above water. They start building their nest from water weeds in April. Two or sometimes three broods of 4–6 eggs are laid and reared. When disturbed, the adult carefully covers the eggs with weeds before leaving the nest. The chicks are able to take to the water as soon as they hatch. They will climb on to their parent's back to hide if an alarm call is given. Like most grebes they are rather weak, clumsy fliers, and because their legs are set so far back for efficient swimming they are ungainly on land.

37. MOORHEN (*Gallinula chloropus*). The moorhen is one of the most ubiquitous wetland birds, breeding wherever there is thick vegetation close to fresh water. Like the little grebe, it is able to stay submerged with only the tip of the bill and its nostrils staying above water. Its high pitched 'kruk' call, its jerky swimming motion, flicking white tail flashes and its red bill with a yellow tip, readily distinguish the moorhen from the coot.

38. MOORHEN (*Gallinula chloropus*) **NEST.** The nest is built in among reeds or sedges, preferably away from the bank. Five to eleven grey-white eggs speckled with red-brown are usually laid. Occasionally two females lay in the same nest. The chicks, which are little black bundles of fluff, can immediately take to the water. But even on the water they are not safe from pike, which take many of them. Moorhens are deceptively clumsy fliers and they soon colonise any suitable wetland area which is created by man. Moorhens are common on the lakes of our city parks. If London is typical, this spread into the cities has been relatively recent. In 1880, moorhens were rare visitors to London, but by the end of the century they were quite common. St James's Park contains over a hundred at the end of the breeding season and many more move in during the winter.

36

37

38

39 ×2

39. PIKE (*Esox lucius*). A small pike such as this could grow into a 15–20 kg monster and become one of the most ferocious predators in British waters. Normally pike lurk motionless beneath lilies or at the edge of reeds. An unsuspecting fish approaches and is snapped up by the pike's furious rush. Spawning takes place in spring and early summer in a quiet shallow area. The males gather nearby and two or three accompany the female in to spawn. Afterwards many of the adults die.